6 Month
Goals and
Accountability
Planner
For Authors

Isbn: 978-0-9977542-3-0

Dokopot Books

Dedication

This planner is dedicated to the
fabulous writers of
**Romance Authors of the
Heartland**.
You inspire me.

How to use this planner

➤ The monthly calendars provide an overview of goals and accomplishments. Writing down your goals keeps them visible and helps you narrow your focus. You're more likely to succeed with written, specific and focused goals.

➤ Use the weekly calendar pages to break down larger goals, record daily word/page counts, and keep yourself moving forward.

➤ Accountability is an important part of staying on track to meet your goals. Use this planner to track anything and everything that relates to your career as an author. Use these pages and be accountable to yourself!

➤ Choose an accountability partner or group and report regularly. Accountability works even better when shared.

➤ Keep track of the books you read and reviews you've written for those books. You may be surprised at how much you read. Keep a record of classes, webinars and podcasts, too.

➤ Use the calendar pages to plan social media posts and opportunities. Being an author is more than just writing.

➤ Have fun with this planner! Write yourself encouraging notes with different colored pens, sketch ideas in the margins, use stickers to celebrate accomplishments! Make these pages YOURS!

➤ This planner is dateless, so you can start anytime. The key is to start.

Maybe you're not perfect, but you're willing to actually look at yourself and take some kind of accountability. That's a change. It might not mean that you can turn everything around, but I think there's something incredibly hopeful about that.
~Brie Larson

Month one

_____

Goals for this month

1._____

_____

_____

_____

2._____

_____

_____

_____

3._____

_____

_____

_____

4._____

_____

_____

_____

5._____

_____

_____

_____

Month 1 --

Add the dates to create your monthly calendar

Monday	Tuesday	Wednesday	Thursday

Use the space below the calendar for notes,
reflections, sparks of ideas.

Friday	Saturday	Sunday	Notes

Week of _____

Use these pages to record daily goals,

Daily Goal	Word/page counts	Goals accomplished
Monday		◯
Tuesday		◯
Wednesday		◯
Thursday		◯
Friday		◯

Saturday		◯
Sunday		◯

Weekly Totals:

Monthly Totals:

Year to Date:

Notes and Observations:

Week of _____

Use these pages to record daily goals,

Daily Goal	Word/page counts	Goals accomplished
Monday		○
Tuesday		○
Wednesday		○
Thursday		○
Friday		○

Saturday		◯
Sunday		◯

Weekly Totals: ⬭

Monthly Totals: ⬭

Year to Date: ⬭

Notes and Observations:

Week of _____

Use these pages to record daily goals,

Daily Goal	Word/page counts	Goals accomplished
Monday		◯
Tuesday		◯
Wednesday		◯
Thursday		◯
Friday		◯

Saturday		◯
Sunday		◯

Weekly Totals:

Monthly Totals:

Year to Date:

Notes and Observations:

Week of _____

Use these pages to record daily goals,

Daily Goal	Word/page counts	Goals accomplished
Monday		◯
Tuesday		◯
Wednesday		◯
Thursday		◯
Friday		◯

Saturday		◯
Sunday		◯

Weekly Totals:

Monthly Totals:

Year to Date:

Notes and Observations:

Think about the past month
and your goals.
Does **each** goal matter to you?

You'll be more successful
when you answer the why.

"People lose their way when they lose
their why." ~Gail Hyatt

Books Read This Month

Title and Author
_____
Notes and review:

Title and Author
_____
Notes and review:

Title and Author
_____
Notes and review:

Title and Author
_____
Notes and review:

Title and Author
_____
Notes and review:

Title and Author
_____
Notes and review:

Title and Author
_____
Notes and review:

Title and Author
_____
Notes and review:

Add more books to this page as needed. Or use the space for creative doodling. Have Fun!

Accountability

My accountability partner(s):

☆ Week one report

☆ Week two report

☆ Week three report

☆ Week four report

End of month report

Observations and notes for next month

I'm pretty disciplined to keep the momentum of a story going by writing everyday, even if it's only a couple paragraphs or a page or two.

~James Rollins

Month two

_____

Goals for this month

1._____

_____

_____

_____

2._____

_____

_____

_____

3._____

_____

_____

_____

4._____

_____

_____

_____

5._____

_____

_____

_____

Month 2

Add the dates to create your monthly calendar

Monday	Tuesday	Wednesday	Thursday

Use the space below the calendar for notes, reflections, sparks of ideas.

Friday	Saturday	Sunday	Notes

Week of _____

Use these pages to record daily goals,

Daily Goal	Word/page counts	Goals accomplished
Monday		○
Tuesday		○
Wednesday		○
Thursday		○
Friday		○

Saturday		◯
Sunday		◯

Weekly Totals:

Monthly Totals:

Year to Date:

Notes and Observations:

Week of _____

Use these pages to record daily goals,

Daily Goal	Word/page counts	Goals accomplished
Monday		⬭
Tuesday		⬭
Wednesday		⬭
Thursday		⬭
Friday		⬭

Saturday		◯
Sunday		◯

Weekly Totals:

Monthly Totals:

Year to Date:

Notes and Observations:

Week of _____

Use these pages to record daily goals,

Daily Goal	Word/page counts	Goals accomplished
Monday		◯
Tuesday		◯
Wednesday		◯
Thursday		◯
Friday		◯

Saturday		
Sunday		

Weekly Totals:

Monthly Totals:

Year to Date:

Notes and Observations:

Week of _____

Use these pages to record daily goals,

Daily Goal	Word/page counts	Goals accomplished
Monday		◯
Tuesday		◯
Wednesday		◯
Thursday		◯
Friday		◯

Saturday		◯
Sunday		◯

Weekly Totals: ⬭

Monthly Totals: ⬭

Year to Date: ⬭

Notes and Observations:

Think about the past month
and your goals.
Does **each** goal matter to you?

You'll be more successful
when you answer the why.

"People lose their way when they lose
their why." ~Gail Hyatt

Books Read This Month

Title and Author

Notes and review:

Title and Author

Notes and review:

Title and Author

Notes and review:

Title and Author

Notes and review:

Title and Author

Notes and review:

Title and Author

Notes and review:

Title and Author

Notes and review:

Title and Author

Notes and review:

Add more books to this page as needed. Or use the space for creative doodling. Have Fun!

Accountability

My accountability partner(s):

⯐ Week one report

⯐ Week two report

⯐ Week three report

⯐ Week four report

End of month report

Observations and notes for next month

You'll only achieve
what you
intentionally

pursue.
~ Michael Hyatt

Month three

_____

Goals for this month

1._____

_____

_____

_____

2._____

_____

_____

_____

3._____

_____

_____

_____

4._____

_____

_____

_____

5._____

_____

_____

_____

Month 3 -

Add the dates to create your monthly calendar

Monday	Tuesday	Wednesday	Thursday

Use the space below the calendar for notes,
reflections, sparks of ideas.

Friday	Saturday	Sunday	Notes

Week of _____

Use these pages to record daily goals,

Daily Goal	Word/page counts	Goals accomplished
Monday		◯
Tuesday		◯
Wednesday		◯
Thursday		◯
Friday		◯

Saturday		
		◯

Sunday		
		◯

Weekly Totals:

Monthly Totals:

Year to Date:

Notes and Observations:

Week of _____

Use these pages to record daily goals,

Daily Goal	Word/page counts	Goals accomplished
Monday		◯
Tuesday		◯
Wednesday		◯
Thursday		◯
Friday		◯

Saturday		◯
Sunday		◯

Weekly Totals: ⬭

Monthly Totals: ⬭

Year to Date: ⬭

Notes and Observations:

Week of _____

Use these pages to record daily goals,

Daily Goal	Word/page counts	Goals accomplished
Monday		◯
Tuesday		◯
Wednesday		◯
Thursday		◯
Friday		◯

Saturday		◯
Sunday		◯

Weekly Totals: ⬭

Monthly Totals: ⬭

Year to Date: ⬭

Notes and Observations:

Week of _____

Use these pages to record daily goals,

Daily Goal	Word/page counts	Goals accomplished
Monday		◯
Tuesday		◯
Wednesday		◯
Thursday		◯
Friday		◯

Saturday		◯
Sunday		◯

Weekly Totals: ⬭

Monthly Totals: ⬭

Year to Date: ⬭

Notes and Observations:

Think about the past month
and your goals.
Does **each** goal matter to you?

You'll be more successful
when you answer the why.

"People lose their way when they lose
their why." ~Gail Hyatt

Books Read This Month

Title and Author

Notes and review:

Title and Author

Notes and review:

Title and Author

Notes and review:

Title and Author

Notes and review:

Title and Author

Notes and review:

Title and Author

Notes and review:

Title and Author

Notes and review:

Title and Author

Notes and review:

Add more books to this page as needed. Or use
the space for creative doodling. Have Fun!

Accountability

My accountability partner(s):

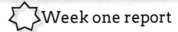Week one report

Week two report

Week three report

Week four report

End of month report

Observations and notes for next month

Keep writing. Try to do a little bit every day, even if the result looks like crap. Getting from page four to page five is more important than spending three weeks getting page four perfect.
~Alan Dean Foster

Month four

_____

Goals for this month

1._____

_____

_____

_____

2._____

_____

_____

_____

3._____

_____

_____

_____

4._____

_____

_____

_____

5._____

_____

_____

_____

Month 4

Add the dates to create your monthly calendar

Monday	Tuesday	Wednesday	Thursday

Use the space below the calendar for notes, reflections, sparks of ideas.

Friday	Saturday	Sunday	Notes

Week of _____

Use these pages to record daily goals,

Daily Goal	Word/page counts	Goals accomplished
Monday		◯
Tuesday		◯
Wednesday		◯
Thursday		◯
Friday		◯

Saturday		
		◯
Sunday		
		◯

Weekly Totals:

Monthly Totals:

Year to Date:

Notes and Observations:

Week of _____

Use these pages to record daily goals,

Daily Goal	Word/page counts	Goals accomplished
Monday		◯
Tuesday		◯
Wednesday		◯
Thursday		◯
Friday		◯

Saturday		◯
Sunday		◯

Weekly Totals: ⬭

Monthly Totals: ⬭

Year to Date: ⬭

Notes and Observations:

Week of _____

Use these pages to record daily goals,

Daily Goal	Word/page counts	Goals accomplished
Monday		◯
Tuesday		◯
Wednesday		◯
Thursday		◯
Friday		◯

Saturday		◯
Sunday		◯

Weekly Totals: ⬭

Monthly Totals: ⬭

Year to Date: ⬭

Notes and Observations:

Week of _____

Use these pages to record daily goals,

Daily Goal	Word/page counts	Goals accomplished
Monday		◯
Tuesday		◯
Wednesday		◯
Thursday		◯
Friday		◯

Saturday		◯
Sunday		◯

Weekly Totals:

Monthly Totals:

Year to Date:

Notes and Observations:

Think about the past month
and your goals.
Does **each** goal matter to you?

You'll be more successful
when you answer the why.

"People lose their way when they lose
their why." ~Gail Hyatt

Books Read This Month

Title and Author

Notes and review:

Title and Author

Notes and review:

Title and Author

Notes and review:

Title and Author

Notes and review:

Title and Author

Notes and review:

Title and Author

Notes and review:

Title and Author

Notes and review:

Title and Author

Notes and review:

Add more books to this page as needed. Or use the space for creative doodling. Have Fun!

Accountability

My accountability partner(s):

☆ Week one report

☆ Week two report

☆ Week three report

☆ Week four report

End of month report

Observations and notes for next month

Just keep writing, and try to finish that novel. Remember, all authors started exactly where you are right now; the only difference between a published author and a non-published one is that the published author never stopped writing.

~Julie Kagawa

Month five

_____

Goals for this month

1._____

_____

_____

_____

2._____

_____

_____

_____

3._____

_____

_____

_____

4._____

_____

_____

_____

5._____

_____

_____

_____

Month 5

Add the dates to create your monthly calendar

Monday	Tuesday	Wednesday	Thursday

Use the space below the calendar for notes, reflections, sparks of ideas.

Friday	Saturday	Sunday	Notes

Week of _____

Use these pages to record daily goals,

Daily Goal	Word/page counts	Goals accomplished
Monday		◯
Tuesday		◯
Wednesday		◯
Thursday		◯
Friday		◯

Saturday			◯

Sunday			◯

Weekly Totals:

Monthly Totals:

Year to Date:

Notes and Observations:

Week of _____

Use these pages to record daily goals,

Daily Goal	Word/page counts	Goals accomplished
Monday		○
Tuesday		○
Wednesday		○
Thursday		○
Friday		○

Saturday		◯
Sunday		◯

Weekly Totals:

Monthly Totals:

Year to Date:

Notes and Observations:

Week of _____

Use these pages to record daily goals,

Daily Goal	Word/page counts	Goals accomplished
Monday		◯
Tuesday		◯
Wednesday		◯
Thursday		◯
Friday		◯

Saturday		○
Sunday		○

Weekly Totals: ⬭

Monthly Totals: ⬭

Year to Date: ⬭

Notes and Observations:

Week of _____

Use these pages to record daily goals,

Daily Goal	Word/page counts	Goals accomplished
Monday		◯
Tuesday		◯
Wednesday		◯
Thursday		◯
Friday		◯

Saturday		◯

Sunday		◯

Weekly Totals:

Monthly Totals:

Year to Date:

Notes and Observations:

Think about the past month
and your goals.
Does **each** goal matter to you?

You'll be more successful
when you answer the why.

"People lose their way when they lose
their why." ~Gail Hyatt

Books Read This Month

Title and Author

Notes and review:

Title and Author

Notes and review:

Title and Author

Notes and review:

Title and Author

Notes and review:

Title and Author

Notes and review:

Title and Author

Notes and review:

Title and Author

Notes and review:

Title and Author

Notes and review:

Add more books to this page as needed. Or use the space for creative doodling. Have Fun!

Accountability

My accountability partner(s):

⭐Week one report

⭐Week two report

⭐ Week three report

⭐Week four report

End of month report

Observations and notes for next month

Focus!
Man who chases
two rabbits
catches neither.
~Chinese Proverb

Month six

_____

Goals for this month

1._____

_____

_____

_____

2._____

_____

_____

_____

3._____

_____

_____

_____

4._____

_____

_____

_____

5._____

_____

_____

_____

Month 6 _____

Add the dates to create your monthly calendar

Monday	Tuesday	Wednesday	Thursday

Use the space below the calendar for notes,
reflections, sparks of ideas.

Friday	Saturday	Sunday	Notes

Week of _____

Use these pages to record daily goals,

Daily Goal	Word/page counts	Goals accomplished
Monday		◯
Tuesday		◯
Wednesday		◯
Thursday		◯
Friday		◯

Saturday		
Sunday		

Weekly Totals:

Monthly Totals:

Year to Date:

Notes and Observations:

Week of _____

Use these pages to record daily goals,

Daily Goal	Word/page counts	Goals accomplished
Monday		◯
Tuesday		◯
Wednesday		◯
Thursday		◯
Friday		◯

Saturday		◯
Sunday		◯

Weekly Totals: ⬭

Monthly Totals: ⬭

Year to Date: ⬭

Notes and Observations:

Week of _____

Use these pages to record daily goals,

Daily Goal	Word/page counts	Goals accomplished
Monday		◯
Tuesday		◯
Wednesday		◯
Thursday		◯
Friday		◯

Saturday		◯
Sunday		◯

Weekly Totals: ⬭

Monthly Totals: ⬭

Year to Date: ⬭

Notes and Observations:

Week of _____

Use these pages to record daily goals,

Daily Goal	Word/page counts	Goals accomplished
Monday		◯
Tuesday		◯
Wednesday		◯
Thursday		◯
Friday		◯

Saturday		◯
Sunday		◯

Weekly Totals: ◯

Monthly Totals: ◯

Year to Date: ◯

Notes and Observations:

Think about the past month
and your goals.
Does **each** goal matter to you?

You'll be more successful
when you answer the why.

"People lose their way when they lose
their why." ~Gail Hyatt

Books Read This Month

Title and Author
_____
Notes and review:

Title and Author
_____
Notes and review:

Title and Author
_____
Notes and review:

Title and Author
_____
Notes and review:

Title and Author
_____
Notes and review:

Title and Author
_____
Notes and review:

Title and Author
_____
Notes and review:

Title and Author
_____
Notes and review:

Add more books to this page as needed. Or use
the space for creative doodling. Have Fun!

Accountability

My accountability partner(s):

☆ Week one report

☆ Week two report

☆ Week three report

☆ Week four report

End of month report

Observations and notes for next month

You don't
have to be great
to start,
but you have to
start
to be great.
~Zig Zigler

Meet *lizzie starr

*lizzie always made up games and stories to keep her company. So, a cunning witch lived in Grampa's weather research station and was only held at bay by waving a certain weed. An ancient road grader morphed into a boat carrying wild adventurers to islands filled with fierce lions and dangerous cannibals, which really looked a lot like sheep. Now, filled with fantasy, love, and romance with a sparkling twist, the stories of her imagination swirl their way into the mundane world.

Now, because she loves encouraging others to explore their creative side, she also designs journals, planners and activity books.

When *lizzie must return to a more routine life, she's *the Lunch Lady* at a private school.

Author and lunch lady~~what a combination!

Made in the USA
San Bernardino, CA
28 June 2018